Bring Your Dreams to Life

Discover Your Soul's Purpose &
Turn Your Visions into Reality

Jodi Chapman & Dan Teck

Dear Mohamed,
May this be the year
that you bring your
writing dreams to life!
love and
gratitude
Jodi and Dan

DandiLove Unlimited

Ordering information available at:
www.soulfuljournals.com.
For wholesale inquiries, please write to:
info@soulfuljournals.com.
Printed in the United States of America
ISBN: 978-0989313780
Library of Congress Control Number: 2016949435

Table of Contents

Preface:
This Stuff Really Works!

Birth of a Dream

On June 12, 2014, we celebrated our 10-year wedding anniversary by visiting the Oregon coast. The trip was not only a dream come true, it also marked the birth of a new (and much bigger) dream.

At the time, we'd been living in southern Oregon for five years but had never made the three-hour drive to the Pacific. Finally, after years of dreaming and months of planning, we got in the car and headed west. The drive itself was gorgeous – over mountains, through redwood forests, and up the rugged coastline – and the beach itself was every bit as stunning as we'd imagined.

When we first arrived, the weather was a bit nippy, so we bundled up in our sweatshirts, sipped hot chai from our travel mugs, and admired the view from our hotel balcony. Before long, though, the sun burned its way through the clouds, and we headed down to the shore and reveled in the full beachy glory we'd envisioned.

Our most memorable beach moment from the trip came on our way home. We pulled over at a rest stop on Route 101, made the two-minute walk from the parking lot to the beach, and spent the next 90 minutes soaking up the ocean's natural beauty and filling our souls with the soothing-yet-invigorating energy of the waves breaking on the shore and receding back into the ocean.

Those 90 minutes changed our lives forever.

Although we spent less than 24 hours at the coast, we liked it so much that we decided to go back. And next time, we decided, we'd stay longer – maybe for a weekend or even a full week. As we imagined spending an entire week at the beach, it felt so nice that we thought, *Why not spend an entire month?* – and *this* thought felt so appealing that we started imagining how nice it would be to spend *the whole summer*. And this desire grew into our dream to *move* to the beach...forever!

While moving to the beach is certainly a big dream, it came to embody something even bigger than a change of locale, something beyond our love of sand and surf, something more than a quest for the perfect seashell (although we *have* found some pretty nice ones since our move – and, more importantly, we've enjoyed many hours of blissful searching).

Our souls were telling us that this change – after years of physical challenges and personal struggles – would allow us to heal in mind, body, and spirit. This was a place where we could create our ideal lives: making our living as stay-at-home writers while communing with soul-expanding natural beauty on a daily basis. This was a dream that would facilitate the realization of all other dreams.

Nurturing the Dream

For better or worse, though, we couldn't just snap our fingers and *live* this dream immediately. We had business commitments, health concerns, and other obstacles that wouldn't let us pack up and move the next day. But that didn't mean we had to put our dream on hold – we could start the process of bringing it to life right away. The seed had been planted; now it was up to us to water it and nurture it as it grew, even before it appeared above ground and burst into bloom.

Fortunately, we had plenty of dream-nurturing tools at our disposal. After all, we'd spent years immersed in the world of self-help and spirituality – soaking up wisdom and how-to advice from self-help books, inspirational videos, and personal-growth blogs – and we'd just finished writing this book!

Now that we had such a compelling dream, we had a perfect chance to try out everything we'd learned (and written about) in recent years. It was time to put it all to the test and see if this stuff really worked! So we went through the very steps described in this book.

For starters, we knew that this was our soul's calling; and the longer we sat with this dream, the more emphatic our souls became: *This is your path…and, if you follow it, it will lead you to other paths of growth and fulfillment!*

The next step was to align ourselves with this dream. While we were waiting for the externals to align, we didn't have to wait for the *internal* experience – we could *imagine* the beach and *feel* how good it would be to live there.

And that's just what we did: we took daily "trips" to the beach...in our hearts and minds. We'd visualize the sand, the waves, and the sunshine. We'd feel relaxed and happy – just as we'd been during our anniversary trip...and just as we expected to be once we moved there. And we'd exhale and smile.

While these inner vacations felt great immediately, they also had two other huge benefits: they strengthened our confidence that we would bring this dream to life, and they inspired us to take action to turn this vision into reality.

Long before we were in a position to move (or had any housing prospects), we began to live as if it was really happening. We packed most of our belongings and stacked them in the garage; and most of what we didn't pack, we sold on Craigslist. We contacted realtors and kept tabs on the housing market. And we did everything we could to follow our soul's advice: *Be ready.*

As 2014 turned to 2015, however, we had moments of self-doubt: *Should we have taken that so-so house that was available in December? Is this just a pipe dream? Are we ever actually going to do this?*

Despite the lack of external progress (and our wintry surroundings), however, we did our best to stay on a beachy wavelength – surrounding ourselves with beach-themed vision boards, continuing our daily "inner vacations," acting "as if," and knowing that everything was unfolding in divine timing…even if our human minds couldn't quite figure out when that might be.

As time went on, our visualizations got more and more specific – including imagining spending Christmas Day of 2015 on the beach. We didn't know *how* it was going to happen; we just sensed that, somehow, it *would*.

And it did.

Divine Timing

On November 17, 2015, while still living in southern Oregon, we launched our first collaborative book (*365 Ways to Connect with Your Soul*) – a massive undertaking that culminated in a 12-hour live event and a promotional campaign that reached well over a million people. The experience was richly rewarding, incredibly fulfilling, and absolutely exhausting. Forget about moving to another house – we hardly moved *period* for the next two weeks!

In retrospect, it would've been nearly impossible to move before this launch. Clearly, the universe knew this, because it had given us exactly zero housing prospects all year. Two weeks after the launch, however, it must have known that we were ready – because the perfect place in the perfect location became available December 1. We immediately drove up to see it, signed the papers the next day, moved December 23, and spent Christmas Day on the beach!

The dream that we'd nurtured for a year and a half had become a reality.

Living the Dream & Sharing the Dream

We wanted to share this experience here for two reasons: First of all, because living this dream makes us incredibly happy, and we like to share our happiness with others! Even more than this, though, we want to offer evidence that all the feel-good words and processes that we share in this book are more than just words...*they're real!* All the teachings about visualization, manifestation, raising your vibration, and going to the "feeling place" of a dream even before it becomes an external reality – *this stuff really works!*

Our dream-come-true experience is "Exhibit A" (or perhaps we should say "Exhibit B" for *beach*!), and the reality has turned out to be even better than the dream! Not only do we go to the beach almost every day (including earlier today!), but we also enjoy kayaking, hiking, and appreciating the local wildlife (including numerous seagulls as well as bald eagles, gray whales, and sea lions – all of whom make regular appearances at our local beaches).

More than this, the change in location and lifestyle has dramatically improved almost every aspect of our lives, including our health, happiness, and creative inspiration (these words being another "Exhibit B"...for *book*!).

So we can speak from personal experience when we say that these words are more than just words – they're reality for us, and we'd love for them to be for you as well.

While your dreams may be very different from ours (especially if you're not a beach-lover), the same principles can make them come true. You can discover (and listen to) your soul's calling. You can get into alignment with your dream (by visualizing it and going to the "feeling place" even before you take any external action). You can maintain faith that, in divine timing, you too can turn your visions into reality.

And you will.

With love and gratitude,
Jodi & Dan

Introduction:
What's YOUR Dream?

D o you have a dream that you yearn to live?
Having a dream is wonderful. It inspires you and calls you toward your highest destiny. But *having* a dream is very different from *living* your dream. It's the difference between longing to visit a dreamy tourist destination and actually going there…or perhaps even *living* there!

This book helps you make the journey from wherever you are now to wherever your dreams are calling you. It serves as a GPS for your soul, a supportive traveling companion, and a guidebook that helps you enjoy every step of the way.

But how do you undertake such a big, important journey? Where do you even start?

A Three-Part Journey

You can start this journey *right here* and *right now*, from wherever you happen to be! And, to make it less daunting and more manageable (and fun!), we've divided it into three parts:

Part I: *Your Soul's Calling* – Discover (or clarify or reinforce) why you're here. In this step of the process, you'll explore some of life's most important questions and uncover some of your soul's most profound answers.

Part II: *Soulful Alignment* – In this part, you'll get your heart, mind, body, and soul all working together, facing in the direction of your soul's calling, and flowing toward your dreams.

Part III: *Turn Your Visions into Reality* – Here's where you'll take your big calling, turn it into a specific dream, and then start bringing your dream to life! You'll get to experience aspects of your ideals immediately while setting yourself up for ongoing success!

How to Use This Book

Each of the book's three parts contains 50 writing prompts, which you can respond to in the space below each question or in a separate journal. Feel free to work through this material at your own pace, writing as much or as little as you'd like and taking time for reflection as needed.

You can also use these prompts as a springboard for conversations with friends, your partner, or a coach or counselor. Or, if you'd like, you could use this book as the basis for a personal retreat – setting aside a day or a weekend dedicated to this potentially life-transforming process.

Whether you're planning on diving into this book for an entire weekend or just an hour (or less), you'll probably find it helpful to create an atmosphere where you can dream freely. You can go to a quiet room, a peaceful spot outdoors, or any place where you can read, write, and dream undisturbed. If necessary, tell others that you won't be available during this time – just as if you had an extremely important appointment or were in a high-level meeting...which you are: you're meeting with your soul!

If you have a special ritual – such as lighting a candle or saying a prayer – you might find that it helps to create an inspiring inner and outer atmosphere. Feel free to do anything that invites your dream into your heart and welcomes it into your life.

Listen to your inner guidance, and remember: there's no wrong way to do this! Whatever setting you create and however you decide to interact with this material will be just right for you.

What Makes This Book Different?

Although we're here to guide you along the journey, we don't claim to know the specifics of *your* dream – that's between you and your soul! Only you can know what you want, what feels right to you, and what feels like a dream come true.

So we're not going to tell you what you "should" be wanting or moving toward. What we *will* do is offer thought-provoking questions and writing prompts that inspire you to get in touch with your own inner wisdom.

In this way, this book is one part journal/workbook and one part conversation between you and your soul.

That's why we leave plenty of space below each question/prompt – so that you've got room to explore your dreams and to get in touch with your soul.

After all, this isn't just a way to record what you already know – it's a voyage of discovery! And, as we've discovered in our own lives, if you simply show up and put pen to paper (or fingers to keyboard…or even simply mull over the questions within your mind), your soul will reveal its depth and its wisdom to you. So allow yourself free rein to explore and play and let your soul's wisdom flow – you may be amazed at what you discover!

Enjoy the Journey!

We're so excited for you to be setting off on your journey of self-discovery and dream-realization. And it truly is *your* journey – not *ours*. We don't want you to take *our* journey – we want you to take your own! But we *will* be there every step of the way as, together, we navigate the way to the dreams that fill you with joy, bring you more fully to life, and make your soul sing!

As you take this journey into your dreams, please remember to enjoy the process, stay open to pleasant surprises, and have fun! Also, remember what an important, heroic journey you're embarking on. Your dreams have the power to enrich your life, uplift those you love, and transform the world!

It is our profound wish that this book will inspire and support you as you follow your soul's calling and bring your dreams to life! It's also our wish that, as you do, you will give birth to even more beautiful dreams, which you will then fulfill – and which, in turn, will give birth to other dreams…and the process will repeat forever!

Even beyond the birth and fulfillment of your most wonderful dreams, we wish for you to connect with your soul – the deep wisdom within you that is your truest, highest self – because we know that *this* will be your greatest traveling companion of all, one that you can rely on forever…wherever your journey may lead.

Part I:

Your Soul's Calling

H ave you ever wondered why you're here? Do you feel called to live the life of your dreams…even if you're not completely sure what exactly those dreams are? Do you ever wish that someone – perhaps your own soul – could just tell you your purpose?

Well, it can! All you have to do is ask the questions and then be open to hearing the answers that come from your soul – that deep part of you that contains all the wisdom you will ever need.

But how do you get in touch with your soul, and what questions should you ask it? That's where Part I of this book comes in! In this part, you'll find 50 thought-provoking writing prompts that guide you lovingly and soulfully toward your highest calling and your deepest dreams.

The prompts in this part are divided into four sections:

Section I: *Soulful First Impressions* helps you bypass your logical mind and tap straight into your soul's wisdom.

Section II: *A Lifetime of Soulful Clues* explores the guidance that your soul has been whispering (or perhaps, at times, *shouting*) to you throughout your life.

Section III: *Your Heart's Desires* allows your soulful imagination to soar into the future and the dream life you're creating for yourself.

Section IV: *Clarify Your Calling* helps you to further explore, hone, and expand upon the wisdom you've revealed during this process – arriving at a stronger, clearer sense of your soul's calling…and then preparing to answer that call!

As with the rest of this book, remember to move through these prompts at a comfortable pace, sharing your thoughts and responses with others or keeping them to yourself – whatever feels right to you.

However you interact with these prompts, you'll benefit tremendously from their intention: to guide you to a clearer sense of who you are, why you're here, and the life you were born to live.

We hope that these prompts help you explore your deep inner wisdom, make sense of the insight it provides, and emerge with an inspiring vision of your soul's calling!

Section I:
Soulful First Impressions

Sometimes wisdom emerges slowly, after much thought, reflection, and deliberation. Other times, however, your first impressions may be spot on!

With this in mind, answer the questions in this section quickly – before you have time to over-think, analyze, or censor yourself. Write down the first things that come to mind, setting aside questions of practicality, society's expectations, responsibilities, what you think you "should" say, or anything that might interfere with you hearing your soul's voice.

You'll have plenty of time afterwards to reflect and revise. This is your chance to tap directly into your soul – that infinite wisdom inside you that transcends logic, data, and even explanation – allowing this wisdom to flow through you and onto the page.

Discovering your soul's calling might be a long process of excavation, or it might be the very first thing that comes to mind! In either case, we hope that this first section provides you with a clearer sense of your starting point as you set out on this journey of self-discovery.

What is your soul's calling?

Answer this question with the first thing that comes to mind – before you have time to censor yourself. Quick! Write!

What else might be your soul's calling?

Write down five (or more) other possibilities – things that *might* be your soul's calling...or at least *part* of it. (Remember, you can have more than one calling, and each calling has different elements to it. For instance, you might feel a calling to uplift and nurture others and also to express your creative self. And you might feel called to do these things in various roles, such as being a writer, a public speaker, and a mother. The possibilities are endless – and only your soul will know if something is truly calling to you.)

A Noble Calling

What possible callings would you find extremely noble (e.g., finding loving homes for orphans, saving endangered species, or protecting the planet)? What is it about these possible callings that makes them seem noble to you?

An Enjoyable Calling

Now, for the moment, put aside any notions of "noble" or "worthwhile" callings, and just think about what you would *really enjoy*. What calling would you have the most fun fulfilling (e.g., reviewing gourmet restaurants, petting cats, traveling the world)? What would you like your soul's calling to be if you didn't have to factor anyone or anything else into the equation?

Which possibilities bring up the most emotion?

Of the possible callings you've written on the previous pages, which ones excite you, scare you, or bring up strong emotion or energy of any kind?

What if you had to pick just one?

If you had to choose one calling from your previous lists (especially the last two – the ones that strongly appeal to you or bring up the most energy), which would it be?

What if this really is your calling?

How might your life look — and *feel* — if you were living this calling? Describe some possible scenes from this life *as if you were already living it.*

What's missing?

Are there any significant parts of you that would feel left out of the calling you've just described? If so, what are they, and how could you incorporate them into your calling?

A Concise Calling

How would you summarize the (possible) calling you've come up with so far? Can you put it into a few short sentences, a single sentence, or even a single concise phrase?

Any last first impressions?

Before you begin the next step of your soul-discovery process, write down anything else that your soul wants you to know about the possibilities you've already written or considered – or anything else related to your soul's calling.

Section II:
A Lifetime of Soulful Clues

As helpful as first impressions can be, you don't have to limit your soul-searching to this single moment. You can explore the whispers, shouts, and clues that your soul has been offering you throughout your entire life! And then you can take your time to reflect upon these clues at your own comfortable pace as you uncover the wisdom they hold for you today and moving forward.

In our own lives, for instance, we've been giving and receiving clues about inspirational writing almost from the time we could talk…or sing! As a very young child, Jodi would regale her family with impromptu songs of "I don't want to hate you, I just want to love you." Dan also created his own songs, including childhood "hits" such as "Maybe Someday I'll Know" and "Searching" (featuring lyrics such as "What was the meaning of my birth? Why was I put here on this Earth?" and "All I've ever been searching for is me" – penned at the tender age of 12)!

As we got a bit older, our soulful expression shifted more toward the written word – as Jodi focused on writing and editing in college and Dan pursued spiritual writing in college and in various writing groups throughout his 20s. Only in recent years have these interests coalesced into a career, but the calling has been popping up in various forms for decades!

Now it's your turn to explore your own life and the clues that have been emerging over the years. The questions and prompts in this section will help you consider the guidance that *your* soul has been offering you from the time you were a child right up to your present life. And you'll see that your soul has been calling to you all along!

Your Happy List

Write down 20 (or more) things that make you happy – from the big (like loving relationships and good health) to the small (like feeling the ocean breeze or reading a great book).

Happy-List Highlights

Go through your happy list and pick out the top five items that stand out the most – the things that really light you up and make you feel downright giddy! What do you like most about them? What about them really resonates with you? How could you create a dream/calling out of them? (For example, if one of your answers is writing, then you could be a novelist, a blogger, a poet, an ecourse creator, etc.)

When I Grow Up...

When you were a kid, what did you say when people asked you, "What do you want to be when you grow up?" How did that answer change over the years? How would you answer that question now?

Childhood Fun

As a child, what did you do for fun? What were your favorite games, hobbies, or activities?

Adult Fun

What have been some of your favorite games, hobbies, or activities as an adult? What are your current favorites?

Childhood Treasures

As a child, what were your favorite possessions or physical objects (e.g., your bike, a set of paints, or the family piano)?

Adult Treasures

As an adult, what have been some of your favorite possessions or physical objects (e.g., your car, a set of sculpting tools, or a favorite writing desk)? Which objects are among your current favorites?

Jobs and Hobbies

Which of your jobs or hobbies have you been most passionate about? What aspect(s) of them have you enjoyed the most?

Obsessions

Throughout your life, what have you thought about or done obsessively? What about now? What are your current preoccupations or recurring thoughts/actions?

Fully Alive and Energized

What fills you with energy and makes you feel fully alive when you do it – or even *think* about doing it?

Let It Flow

When in your life have you felt a sense of flow –
when things came naturally and moved along with ease
and grace? When have you felt this most recently?

It's Definitely NOT…

What are some things that are definitely NOT your soul's calling? Write down anything you dislike, complain about, or avoid like the plague!

The Opposite of Bad

Look at your previous list and write down things that are the opposite of (or at least very different from) those complaints, onerous tasks, or other unappealing activities.

(For example, if you frequently complain about being micromanaged by your boss, the opposite of that would be to have a great deal of freedom and autonomy in your work and in the rest of your life. This might manifest through being self-employed or working with others who grant you a tremendous amount of freedom and encourage – rather than stifle – your creativity.)

Your Gifts

What unique gifts were you given to share with the world? How do you think you're meant to share them?

Your Values

What is most important to you? What do you admire in others? What values do you strive to embody in your own life (e.g., loyalty, bravery, spirituality, creativity)?

Heroes, Role Models, and You

Write down at least five people you deeply admire – people who you feel have, to a large extent, discovered their souls' callings and are living their dreams. Next to each hero's name, write down what you have in common with them.

Your Most Appealing Hero

Review your previous list and pick the person whose life appeals to you the most. What is their life like? What elements of their life/calling appeal to you? What parts (if any) would you like to be different about *your* life?

Your Message

If you could share a message with the world, what would it be (e.g., "Life doesn't have to be a struggle" or "Love is all that truly matters")?

Your Mission

What do you think is your life's mission? (For example, Jodi's is: "I am here to love fully and freely and to help others do the same." Dan's is: "I am here to express my true self, appreciate the world around me and within me, participate in the joyous expansion of all that is, and inspire others to discover and live their own soul's calling.")

Recurring Themes

Flip back over your answers from this section and reflect upon the soulful "clues" you've received throughout your life. What recurring themes or messages do you notice? Which of these themes resonate the most with you? Which ones do you think are part of your soul's calling?

External Clues

As you reflect upon the externals of your life (e.g., favorite jobs, hobbies, activities, and possessions), how do the details shed light upon your soul's calling? (For example, if your favorite childhood possession was your piano, your favorite job was working at a record store, and your hero is a singer, there's a good chance that music is part of your soul's calling!)

Internal Clues

As you reflect upon the internal aspects of your life (e.g., recurring thoughts, emotions, or spiritual experiences), how do they shed light upon your soul's calling? (For example, what does it say about your soul's calling if you frequently experience – or long to experience – Zen-like tranquility…or if you have recurring thoughts of high-adrenaline activities and situations?)

Revised Calling

Based on everything you've written and reflected on throughout this section, what do you now think is your soul's calling? Have you revised the first-impression answer you gave in Section I? If so, how? If not, how have your reflections reinforced your original answer?

Section III:
Your Heart's Desires

The years of your life can certainly shed light on your soul's calling. However, the point of this book isn't merely to look back on your past or even to reflect on your present life and summarize what already is. While this can offer useful insights, the main point here is to look *forward* – to consider how your soul's calling can guide you as you move ahead with your life and step into your deepest dreams.

This is exactly what you'll be doing in this section: looking ahead. And because the future hasn't happened yet, you have *carte blanche* to speculate, imagine, and dream! After all, *you* are the creator of your own dream – and *you* are the one who gets to live it!

How would you like to feel?

Regardless of your dream life's externals, how would you like your calling to make you *feel*? How would you feel if you were living your dream? (For example, would you feel peaceful, confident, or enthusiastic?)

What would you like to have?

If you were living your dream – your soul's calling –
what are some things that you might have?

What would you like to do?

If you were living your dream – your soul's calling – what are some things that you might do? (This can include one-time experiences [such as going on an expedition to the South Pole] as well as ongoing activities [such as switching careers, taking up a new hobby, or playing your favorite sport every day].)

Living Your Calling…for the Rest of Your Life

Imagine that this process is a complete success: you discover your soul's calling and live your dreams for the rest of your life! Now imagine that you're near the end of your life, reflecting back on many years of personal satisfaction, success (however you define it), and spiritual fulfillment. What are your thoughts, feelings, and memories about this life well lived?

Living Your Calling...10 Years from Now

Again, imagine that you discover your soul's calling and live your dreams. Now, this time, imagine that it's 10 years from now. After a decade of living your dreams, you take stock of your life: what it looks like, how you feel, the externals (where you live, people in your life, etc.), and any other elements of this dream come true. Describe this life, as if it's 10 years from now and you're living this glorious dream.

Living Your Calling…One Year from Now

Once again, imagine that you discover your soul's calling and live your dreams. But this time, mentally fast-forward only one year into the future. After 12 months of living your dreams, describe your life – internals, externals, and any other elements of this dream come true.

Living Your Calling...Today!

If you were already living your soul's calling, what would your life be like right now? How would you describe this life as if you were already living it? What would be different from and what would be the same as the life you're currently living?

External Clues from the Future

As you envision the externals of your dream life from the future (e.g., where you live, what you own, and what you do), how do the imagined details shed light upon your soul's calling? (For example, if you imagine living in a remote natural area or a bustling metropolis, what would these visions/desires say about you, your dream, and your soul's calling?)

Internal Clues from the Future

As you imagine the internal aspects of your dream life from the future (e.g., your emotions and your spiritual experiences), how do these details shed light upon your soul's calling? (For example, what would it say about your soul's calling if you imagine experiencing passionate enthusiasm, Zen-like tranquility, or other states of being?)

Revised Calling

Based on everything you've written and reflected on throughout this section, what do you now think is your soul's calling?

Have you revised the first-impression answer you gave in Section I and the revised version you gave at the end of Section II? If so, how? If not, how have your reflections reinforced your previous answers?

Section IV:
Clarify Your Calling

By this point, you may have a crystal-clear vision of your soul's calling. But, then again, maybe you don't – and that's perfectly fine. In either case, you'll continue to hone, expand, and clarify your calling throughout your life.

With this in mind, this final section of Part I isn't about pinpointing your one-and-only, ultimate, final, never-to-change calling – it's about bringing as much clarity to this subject as you can, based on where you are now. It's about reflecting on the previous sections – your initial impressions, your past and present, and possibilities for your future – and finding the pearls of wisdom they reveal. It's about seeing, hearing, and feeling your soul's calling more clearly than ever.

And it's about getting ready to answer that call.

First Impressions, Revisited

Look back at your responses from Section I ("Soulful First Impressions"). What still resonates the most? What answers (if any) would you change now that you've completed Sections II and III?

Your Life, Revisited

Look back at your responses from Section II ("A Lifetime of Soulful Clues"). What parts stand out or resonate the most? How would you summarize the lessons or take-aways from this section?

Your Future, Revisited

Look back at your responses from Section III ("Your Heart's Desires"). What parts stand out or resonate the most? How would you summarize the lessons or take-aways from this section?

Missing Pieces

Are there any important pieces of your life, your dream, your soul, or your calling that you haven't yet touched upon? If so, what are they and how might they fit in with your calling?

Revised Calling

Based on your previous answers (and everything you've written and reflected on throughout this book so far), what do you think is your soul's calling? Have you revised the first-impression answer you gave in Section I or the revised callings from Sections II and III? If so, how? If not, how have your subsequent answers and reflections reinforced your previous answers?

Answering the Call

Now that you've taken the time to write, reflect, and gain clarity about your soul's calling, here is perhaps the most important question of all: *How will you answer this call?*

Reflecting on Your Journey

How has this journey of discovering your soul's calling been for you?

Take some time to reflect on (and write about) your experiences while responding to the prompts in Part I – where you were when you began, where you are now, how it felt for you, what insights you gained, or anything else that came up for you during this process.

Congratulations!

Before moving on to the next part of this book, take a moment to congratulate yourself for making it through the first phase of the dream-realization process! Pat yourself on the back! Celebrate! And know that you've created a strong foundation for your emerging dream life!

Whether you've discovered a clear picture of your calling or just a general sense of who you are and why you're here, one thing is certain: you're moving toward a deeper connection with yourself, your calling, and your dreams.

As the oft-quoted (or paraphrased) saying goes, "Before you climb your ladder of success, make sure it's leaning against the right building." After engaging with the material in Part I, you can be much more confident that your "ladder" is leaning against the "building" of your dreams!

As you take the next step in Part II, you'll make sure that every part of you is lined up with your dreams – so that you'll be able to move naturally and joyfully into the wonderful life that your soul is calling you toward!

Part II:

Soulful Alignment

Aligning with Your Soul's Calling

Do you ever feel like different parts of you are moving (or *not moving*) in different directions? Your heart wants to rush forward into your dreams, while your head holds back. Your actions move you toward your goals, but your stubborn old beliefs keep tripping you up. Wouldn't it be great if you could get every part of you working together – moving in perfect harmony and alignment?

This part of the book – "Soulful Alignment" – helps you do exactly that! It helps you align your thoughts, words, actions, emotions, and spiritual life so that every part of you can be on the same team. It helps you flow into a life of ease, fulfillment, and joy. It helps you be the person you want to be and live the life that you long for.

Alignment helps you bridge Part I (where you discovered and clarified your soul's calling) and Part III (where you'll bring that dream-calling to life) – making that connection as smoothly and joyfully as possible.

Part II contains 50 writing prompts – all designed to help you align yourself with your soul's calling – divided into four sections:

Section I: *Ideal Alignment* addresses the question, *Alignment with WHAT?*...and invites you to consider your ideal state of being.

Section II: *Internal Alignment* explores your inner life and helps you experience greater harmony with every part of it.

Section III: *External Alignment* explores your outer life and helps you find greater harmony with all aspects of it.

Section IV: *Integrated Alignment* is where all the separate aspects of your inner and outer life/self come together for a "round-table discussion" – with your soul as the mediator and ultimate decision-maker!

Why is alignment so important?

As we mentioned at the end of Part I, before you climb the "ladder" to your dreams, you want to make sure that it's leaning against the right "building." You also want to make sure that every part of you is lined up with the ladder and heading in the same direction. (It could be pretty slow going if you took two steps forward and one step back – and let's not even think about what might happen if, halfway up the ladder, you took one step forward and one step to the left!)

Don't worry – there are no dire consequences if you're not fully aligned; the journey simply won't be as smooth and enjoyable as you'd like it to be. But if the thought of falling from a ladder (even a metaphorical one) concerns you, perhaps you can think of alignment in terms of a more benign (and silly) metaphor.

The Many Legs of Your Dream Journey

Have you ever seen two people dressed up in a horse costume? Think about what would happen if the person in the front moved in a different direction from the person in the back (or one of them moved while the

other stood still). The results would be fairly comical —
except perhaps to the people in the costume!

Now imagine if, instead of two people dressed up as
a horse, 50 people dressed up as a *centipede*. If they
weren't all working together, things could get pretty
hairy pretty quickly! So, before those 50 people start
moving, it would definitely behoove them all to take
some to time to make sure they're all facing the same
direction, getting ready to move at a pace that's
comfortable for everyone, and in agreement about their
common goal.

And that's what you're going to do here in Part II —
take some time to make sure that the different parts of
you are facing the same direction and working in
harmony toward a common goal.

Much like the centipede, the journey of bringing
your dreams to life involves many "legs" — many
moving (or, as the case may be, *not* moving) pieces that
can either work together or trip each other up at every
step of the way.

Whether or not you've thought about it in terms of
"alignment" (or misalignment) you've almost certainly
experienced this sensation — and have probably
observed it in others as well. For example, when
someone says, "I'm my own worst enemy," what this
means is that at least one part of them (such as a harsh
inner critic or an unhealthy behavior) is not in alignment
with their soul. When the different parts of your life
work together, however, you become your own *best
friend*…and your journey can be a dream come true!

Alignment = Harmony and Cooperation

Before you begin the process of aligning with your soul's calling, we wanted to offer one final clarification (and one final metaphor): Being in alignment doesn't mean that every part of your life is uniform, identical, or doing exactly the same thing at the same time. After all, you're a rich, complex person living a rich, complex life – and we wouldn't want to change that!

Alignment simply means that the various parts of your life are interacting in harmony and cooperation – much like a symphony orchestra being guided by a master conductor. Not every instrument plays the same note at the same time, but they do play notes that blend well together to create a rich sonic tapestry. Sometimes, one instrument plays a solo while the others rest (or play quietly to support the soloist).

Likewise, sometimes your heart will lead the way, quietly supported by your logical mind. At other times, you might be called to modify your behavior to accommodate shifts in beliefs. And sometimes you might have to take a break to get back in tune or make sure that every part of you is on the same page (much like a conductor might double-check that every member of the orchestra is playing the same part of the same piece at the same time).

When your soul leads the way and all parts of your life work together to support your calling and your dreams, you can make beautiful music that's a joy to play and a pleasure to hear.

Working Together

Whether you think of alignment in terms of a ladder, a centipede, an orchestra, or any other metaphor that resonates with you, the idea is the same: to get the inner and outer aspects of your life working together to help you bring your dreams to life.

And that's exactly what the questions and writing prompts in Part II are designed to help you do. We hope that these prompts – and your responses to them – help you experience greater alignment with every part of yourself, reap the many benefits of this alignment, and feel good throughout the process.

Section I:
Ideal Alignment

If you want to experience alignment, a good first question to ask yourself is: *Alignment with WHAT?*

(This would be like the orchestra conductor asking, "What piece of music are we going to play?" or the head of the 50-person centipede asking, "Where are we going?" – good questions to ask before you dive headlong into action!)

What do *you* want to align with in your own life? What are you lining up with, pointing at, and preparing to move toward? Is it something you even *want* to align with? Is it worthy of your highest self? Is it worthy of your life? Is it a reflection of your most positive values, beliefs, and ideals? Or, to put it in terms of Part I: *Is it lined up with your soul's calling?*

Before you start to act, make adjustments, or even look at where you are right now, take some time to consider your *ideal* scenarios for each area of your life. This will provide an inner "North Star" to guide you as you move forward into greater and greater alignment.

Ideal Alignment

Imagine that you're already "There" – in that place where you're perfectly aligned: Your body, mind, and spirit work in harmony. Your external life matches your internal experiences. You're living the dream. Describe what this ideal life looks like and feels like for you.

(Note: If you still feel called to the "Revised Calling" you described near the end of Part I, you can reinforce and elaborate on it here. Or, if something different is calling to your soul now, feel free to describe your current ideal vision and what it would feel like to be living it now.)

Emotional Alignment

Let's dig deeper into your previous answer, taking a closer look at the emotional component. In your ideally aligned life, how would you feel (e.g., mostly calm, energized, passionate, or a full range of emotions that flow naturally from one to another)?

Mental Alignment

Again, let's dig deeper into the picture of your ideally aligned life, this time taking a closer look at the mental component. In this ideal life, how would you think, and what would be your most common thoughts (or types of thoughts – e.g., focused thoughts, sharp intellect, habitual positive affirmations, or perhaps fewer thoughts and a clearer mind)?

Spiritual Alignment

Once more, let's dig deeper into the picture of your ideally aligned life, this time taking a closer look at the spiritual component. In your vision of this ideal life, what would your spiritual experience(s) be (e.g., deep connection with the Divine and/or your own soul, significant involvement in a spiritual community, or a solitary practice/experience)?

Physical Alignment

In your ideally aligned life, what would your physical condition/experience(s) be (e.g., at your ideal weight, strong and energized, able to run marathons, healthy internal organs)?

Environmental Alignment

In your ideally aligned life, what would your environment/surroundings be (e.g., your home, the part of the country where you live, the surrounding natural or urban setting)?

Social Alignment

In your ideally aligned life, what would your social situation/experience(s) be (e.g., friendships, romantic relationships, active social life, or generally solitary)?

Material/Financial Alignment

In your ideally aligned life, what is your financial situation and what are your most meaningful material possessions (e.g., multi-millionaire, sports car, modest income, getting by comfortably, fine-art collection, mementos of personal value)?

Action Alignment

In your ideally aligned life, what actions do you perform on a regular basis (e.g., your work, hobbies, vacations)?

Why do you want this?

Why do you want to experience alignment and live the ideal life you've been imagining and describing? What's your motivation and/or inspiration? Write down any reasons – no matter how big, small, or obvious – why you'd like to turn these ideals into reality.

Section II:
Internal Alignment

Now that you have a pretty good idea of what you'd like to align with (and *why*), let's start the process of aligning with it!

In this section, you'll explore your internal life – your thoughts, emotions, values, beliefs, spiritual experiences, and everything else that goes on within your heart, mind, and spirit.

You'll look at where you are now, consider where you'd like to be, and then find ways to get *all* of you facing in that direction.

You'll have the opportunity to get clear about your starting point – and to feel the relief that comes as you lean into greater inner harmony.

Beliefs About Your Ideally Aligned Life

Go back and read your response to the "Ideal Alignment" prompt at the beginning of Section I. What are your beliefs regarding this ideally aligned vision? Do you think that it's a worthwhile dream? Do you believe that you can really experience it? Why or why not?

(For example, you might think that it would be a great life to live, but parts of it – such as driving a fancy sports car – seem a bit frivolous. You might believe that you *can* experience this reality, but that it would take a *lot* of time and effort to achieve. Or you might believe that your ideal reality is already flowing naturally into your experience and will continue to do so! There's no right or wrong answer – just whatever you honestly believe right now.)

Beliefs About Yourself

What are your beliefs about yourself, especially with regard to your ideally aligned life? Do you believe that you're good enough to deserve it, intelligent and talented enough to achieve it, and fortunate enough to live it? Why or why not?

(For example, you might believe that you are a good, deserving person but that you've never been fortunate – you weren't born with a silver spoon in your mouth and you never seem to get any lucky breaks. You might believe that you're not educated enough to reach your dreams. Or perhaps you believe that [to paraphrase Al Franken's old *Saturday Night Live* character, Stuart Smalley] you're good enough, smart enough, and likeable enough to live your dream life. As with the other questions, there's no right or wrong answer – just whatever you honestly believe right now.)

Ideally Aligned Beliefs

What beliefs (whether or not you currently believe them) would be in alignment with your dream life and your highest self? In other words, what beliefs would be most conducive to living your ideal life?

(For example, beliefs that are in alignment with your dream life – and conducive to living it – might include: "I've achieved many goals in the past, so I have every reason to believe that I can and will achieve this goal, too!" or "The universe is conspiring to support me in living my dreams.")

Most Aligned Actual (or Possible) Beliefs

What do you (or *could* you) believe right now that is the most aligned with your ideal life/self? In other words, what's the closest you can currently come to the ideal beliefs you described in the previous question – even if it's just a small step in that direction?

(For example, it might be too much of a stretch to tell yourself, "I achieve everything I want," because you probably wouldn't believe it. [And it actually might backfire if your logical mind responds with a litany of all the things you *haven't* achieved!] But perhaps you could bring yourself to believe something along the lines of: "I achieve *many* of my goals, and I'm confident that I can continue to move closer to my ideals while enjoying the process most of the time.")

Recurring Thoughts

What are some of your most commonly recurring thoughts (whether or not they are directly related to your dream)? Do they tend to be primarily negative (e.g., worried or fearful) or positive (e.g., hopeful or focused on what you appreciate)? Do you think a lot about any one particular aspect of life (e.g., your work, finances, relationship)?

Thoughts About Your Ideally Aligned Life

What are your thoughts regarding the ideally aligned vision you described in Section I? Do you think a lot about ways to live this dream, or do you bemoan the fact that you're not yet doing so?

Thoughts About Yourself

When you think about yourself, what words (or phrases, images, etc.) come to mind?

(For example, you might think of yourself as calm, energized, lazy, ambitious, thoughtful, absent-minded, selfish, or kind. You might see yourself as old and feeble, youthful and vibrant, or in your physical and mental prime.)

Thoughts About Your Ideally Aligned Self

What words would you use to describe someone (real or hypothetical) who was ideally aligned with your ideal vision?

(For example, such a person might be kind, curious, calm, confident, and comfortable in their own skin. They might be someone who appreciates their current life while optimistically looking forward to the future. They might be a mellow, go-with-the-flow type of person, or they might be a take-charge alpha – whatever type of person and qualities appeal most to *you* and fit with *your* ideal vision.)

Best Thoughts About Yourself

What are the best thoughts you could have about yourself? What thoughts are as close as possible to the ideally aligned person you described in the previous answer that are also true about you (at least to some extent)?

(For example, while you might not believe a thought such as "I'm the smartest person in the world," perhaps you can embrace something along the lines of: "I have a good mind, I'm able to learn new things, and I have the ability to experience greater fulfillment in my life.")

Emotional Climate

If moods are like weather, what's your emotional "climate"? Do you tend to be warm and sunny, cold and bitter, or prone to violent emotional "thunderstorms"? In other words, what is your predominant emotional state?

Emotions About Your Surroundings

How do you feel about the people, places, and things that play the biggest role in your life (e.g., your partner and/or family, your home, your work environment)?

Emotions About Yourself

What emotions do you feel most often about yourself (e.g., sad, proud, enthusiastic)?

(This may or may not be different from your emotions about your surroundings described in your previous answer. For example, you might feel great about most of the people around you, but frequently feel critical of yourself – or vice versa: perhaps you often feel depressed when you observe your surroundings but are generally positive and optimistic about yourself.)

Emotional Alignment

What would your emotional experience be like if you were already aligned with your ideal vision and your higher self? What could you do to bring yourself closer to this state?

(For example, perhaps your emotional ideal would be total equanimity in all circumstances. Or maybe it would still include a full range of emotions but a tendency to shift quickly back toward optimism, even when circumstances are challenging – a state you could move toward by practicing appreciation.)

Spiritual High

When have you been at your most aligned spiritually? (You can think of this in religious terms, as a "moment of grace," or as a secular/psychological "peak experience.") Describe the experience and how it felt for you.

Spiritual Norm

How would you describe your typical spiritual state of being?

Spiritual Alignment

What would your spiritual experience be like if you were already living in a state of alignment with your dream and your higher self? What could you do to bring yourself closer to this state?

(For example, you might feel that daily prayer or meditation could deepen your appreciation of the divine and help you feel more connected to your higher self.)

Values

What do you value the most (e.g., security, creativity, serenity)? How are these values reflected in your ideally aligned vision? How are these values reflected (or not reflected) in your current life? How could your life better reflect your most cherished values?

Inspiration

What is your inspiration for wanting to align?

(Note: You can think of *motivation* as an external reason [e.g., wanting to support your family, heal your body, or save a relationship] and *inspiration* as an internal reason [e.g., to be proud of yourself, to experience spiritual serenity, or simply because alignment feels better]. So, to rephrase this question: what *internal* reasons do you have for wanting to experience greater alignment with your highest self/dream?)

Section III:
External Alignment

In this section, you'll explore your external life – your work, finances, home environment, hobbies, activities, material possessions, and the people closest to you. You'll consider how these external aspects currently look and how you can bring them into greater alignment with your ideals.

Sometimes externals change quickly – perhaps even instantaneously! Other times, they can take longer to change (which is often a good thing – allowing change to happen at a comfortable, organic pace). Even in cases of slower changes, however, you can at least *begin* the alignment process in an instant! You can get honest about where you are and start leaning into greater and greater harmony in all areas of your life.

We hope the prompts in this section will inspire you to do exactly that!

Describe your external life.

Setting aside (for now) your thoughts, emotions, and other internal experiences, what does your external life look like now (e.g., where you live, what you do, who you spend your time with)? In what ways is this already aligned with your ideal? In what ways is it different?

Work

Do you currently work? If so, how is your job aligned (or not aligned) with the vision of your highest self/life? If you don't currently work, how is or isn't this aligned with your ideal?

Finances

How would you describe your financial status (e.g., wealthy, struggling, comfortable)? How are your finances aligned (or not aligned) with the vision of your ideal life?

Hobbies/Activities

What do you do for fun? How does (or doesn't) this align with your ideal vision?

Possessions

What are some of your biggest material possessions (in terms of size, expense, or personal significance)? How do (or don't) they align with your ideal vision?

People in Your Life

It's sometimes said that we tend to be the average (in terms of attitude and success) of the five people in our lives the most. Who are the five people most involved in your life – the people who you spend the most time with and communicate with the most? How would you describe their attitudes, beliefs, or other significant qualities? How do (or don't) you share these qualities? How are these qualities aligned (or not) with your ideal?

Health

Describe your physical health and vitality. How does (or doesn't) this reflect your ideal?

Environment

Describe the environment(s) where you spend the most time (e.g., home, work, or frequent travel destinations). How do (or don't) these places reflect your ideal vision?

Motivation

What is your motivation for wanting to align?

(Remember, as we distinguished in Section II, *motivation* is an external reason [e.g., wanting to support your family, heal your body, or save a relationship] and *inspiration* is an internal reason [e.g., to be proud of yourself, to experience spiritual serenity, or simply because alignment feels better]. So, what *external* reasons do you have for wanting to experience greater alignment with your highest self/dream?)

Section IV:
Integrated Alignment

So far you've looked at the various parts of your life one piece at a time – from thoughts and emotions to work and relationships. You've considered your current reality, as well as your ideal vision for these aspects. And you've considered how these pieces are (or aren't) currently aligned with your ideals, your dreams, and your calling.

Now these separate aspects of your life get to sit down together at a round-table discussion where everyone gets to voice their positions, opinions, and suggestions. And then your soul (as the mediator and ultimate decision-maker) gets to find ways to bring these pieces into greater and greater alignment – bringing them into harmony with your ideals.

Round-Table Starting Points

Summarize where you are right now with the major aspects of your life: emotionally, mentally, physically, spiritually, and externally (e.g., relationships, work, home).

(For example, you might write: "I'm generally happy. I feel like I have a sharp mind and a healthy body. I love my spouse and family, and I'm optimistic about the future. The greatest area of dissatisfaction right now concerns my work. I don't feel like I'm pursuing my passion or my calling, and I frequently feel frustrated that I'm just wasting time and squandering my potential. I'd love to find ways to spend more of my life doing what I love.")

Round-Table Ideals

Looking at the same aspects of your life as in the previous question (emotions, physical body, external life, etc.), summarize the ideals of each area (e.g., to be emotionally stable and physically vital).

Proposed Changes

Let the different aspects of your life "speak at the round table" and propose changes that could bring them into closer alignment with your ideals.

(For example, maybe your physical body could propose more joyful movement as a way to increase vitality, or your spiritual self could propose meditating regularly.)

Round-Table Challenges

Are there any aspects of your life that present obstacles to aligning with your highest self/dreams? Let those parts of you bring their doubts or challenges to light.

(For example, perhaps your body and soul are on board, but your mind doesn't believe that you're smart enough to reach your dreams.)

Round-Table Solutions

Address the challenges and concerns from your previous answer. What are some possible solutions or steps that might bring those parts of you into greater alignment?

(For example, if you doubt your own abilities, you could find evidence of your talent and intelligence – such as your academic achievements, success at work, or anything else that might placate your mind's concerns. Or you might take action, such as receiving additional training/education in your area of interest.)

Round-Table Harmony

How are the various aspects of your life/self working in harmony together and complementing one another?

(For example, perhaps your desire not to overwork your body can lead to great emotional equilibrium or mental acuity.)

Minority Report

Are there any parts of you that still resist alignment with your higher self/dream? If so, how might this perspective actually enrich your life?

(For example, perhaps you have faith in the universe and in your abilities to move into greater alignment with your dream life; however, you might have a recurring thought that holds you back, such as, "Successful people always become smug and 'too big for their britches,' and I don't want to be that way!" After acknowledging this thought, you might be able to reassure your mind that you will always value humility, compassion, and other qualities you admire...even as you reach your dreams!)

Your Soul's Perspective

After hearing the various "parties" (aspects of yourself) voice their positions, concerns, and suggestions, let your soul speak its piece. What is its position on the various parts of you and your current life? How does your soul think that you can align these parts in order to best serve your highest self and live your dream life?

(To tap into your soul's perspective, you can imagine it sitting at the "head of the table" or perhaps even floating above the table, viewing the various aspects of your life from a higher, non-attached perspective, able to see the individual pieces as well as how they can all fit together into a harmoniously aligned whole.)

Action Steps

Having heard the perspectives of your soul and the various parts of you (physical, emotional, etc.), what do you think would be the most important steps that you could take to move into greater alignment?

(Note: These might be physical actions, such as exercising regularly, or they might be inner shifts, such as consciously redirecting your thoughts to focus on positive aspects of your life.)

Commitment

How will you implement the action steps you came up with in your previous answer? What commitment will you make to following through with these actions/changes – now and on an ongoing basis?

Outside Support

Who will you get to support you in keeping your commitment to greater alignment? How will they support you (e.g., checking in with an accountability partner or working out with a buddy)?

Intention

As you implement these changes, what is your intention? Do you want to reach a specific goal by a specific date? Do you want to start seeing external evidence of your alignment? Do you want to feel better emotionally? What do you intend to experience as you move into greater alignment?

Closing Remarks

Allow your soul (and/or any other aspects of yourself) to express any final thoughts about your alignment, this process, or anything else that's come up for you as you've gone through this part of the process.

Get ready to live the dream!

As you arrive at the end of Part II, you've gotten in touch with your soul's calling and made sure that every part of you is aligned with it. Now, the only thing left to do is to make your soul's calling your *real life* – to turn your visions into reality, which is exactly what the third and final part of this book is designed to help you do.

As you did after completing Part I, take some time now to look back on your journey up to this point, reflect on how far you've come, and celebrate where you are now.

Then, whenever you're ready, turn the page and get ready to bring your dreams to life!

Part III:

Turn Your Visions into Reality

Welcome to your dream!

Hopefully, by this point, you're feeling good about your soul's calling, you're fully aligned with it, and you're ready to turn your visions into reality – which is exactly what this third and final part of the book is designed to help you do. In the pages that follow, you'll have the opportunity to reinforce what you've learned in the previous two parts, build on those lessons, and implement them into your daily life.

If your calling isn't crystal clear or your alignment still feels a bit shaky at this point, don't worry – you'll have plenty of time to clarify and solidify (or modify) them as you move through Part III (and beyond). And even if you already feel good about what you've discovered in Parts I and II, your dreams will continue to evolve…just like you!

Dreams, Visions, and Callings

In Part I of this book, you explored your soul's calling – the big-picture sense of your life's purpose, the reason why you're here on Earth. In Part II, you aligned yourself with this calling – inside and out. Now, in Part III, you get to take that big picture (which is probably very broad and perhaps a bit abstract) and express it as a specific dream – something that you can envision and actually bring to life.

Everyone has a different dream and a different vision of what it will look like when it comes true. Likewise, everyone has a different *definition* of "dream" – and in this part, you'll get to explore your own. To us, a dream is the life you imagine and desire, a life that would fulfill your soul's calling, embody your life's purpose, and satisfy you at the deepest level. We see the vision of your dream as an inner picture that calls you toward this life – the life that makes you feel the most alive and the most fully *you*.

For example, if your soul's calling is to express your truth and inspire others, your dream might be to become an inspirational author. You might have a vision of becoming a bestseller, reaching millions with your message, and receiving thank-you notes and other signs of appreciation from the many people you've inspired.

Or perhaps you feel called to serve people in need, in which case you might dream of feeding hungry people in your area or around the world. Perhaps your vision is to start a charity or open up a network of shelters or soup kitchens.

If you feel called to share your zest for life through physical expression, you might have a dream of becoming a dancer and a vision of performing in front of an enraptured audience who feels your passion for movement and for life.

Whatever your calling, vision, or dream may be, this final part of the book can help you turn it into a reality.

Sections of the Dream Journey

The journey of making your dreams come true can seem big and overwhelming, but if you break it down into smaller steps, it becomes much more manageable, doable, and fun! With this in mind, the prompts in Part III are divided into three sections:

Section I: *Inviting Your Dream* sets the stage – internally and externally – for the journey you're embarking on, preparing you to welcome your dream into your heart and into your life.

Section II: *Reviewing, Revising, and Reinforcing Your Dream* helps you clarify what your dream truly is – and gets you facing in that direction before you set off on your journey!

Section III: *Living Your Dream* focuses on implementation – not just moving toward your dream, but experiencing it right now, on a day-by-day, moment-by-moment basis!

We hope that these prompts inspire you to turn your visions into reality, to live your dreams, and to enjoy every step along the way!

Section I:
Inviting Your Dream

Living your dream is about honoring every part of your life – including your emotions, your surroundings, and the vision you're moving toward. It's about feeling good and being in a positive place throughout the entire process, starting with your preparation.

With this in mind, let's start by creating an environment that's most conducive to inviting your dream into your heart and bringing it into your life. In this section, you'll get into a good space where you can give yourself permission to dream, set your intention, and prepare yourself (internally and externally) to live your dream.

So, if you're ready to open your heart to the amazing dream that awaits you, turn the page and let's begin this beautiful, powerful process.

Set Your Dream Scene

If you wanted to fall asleep and have a dream, you'd want the conditions to be just right: to be in bed (or somewhere else comfortable), to have the lights off, and not to be disturbed by noises or interruptions. Similarly, as you start bringing your *waking* dream to life, you want a setting that's as conducive to this as possible.

So, if you haven't already done so, take some time right now to create an atmosphere that best supports your dream. Go to a special place. Tell others that you don't want to be disturbed for however long you're setting aside. Get comfortable. And get ready to dream...and to bring that dream to life!

Describe the setting you've created, how it makes you feel, and how it helps you start bringing your dream to life.

Be Here Now

Now that you've created an external environment that's conducive to bringing your dream to life, take some time to become fully present in this place – and within yourself.

With your eyes open or closed, take a few deep breaths. Feel your abdomen expand and contract with each breath. Feel any tension slipping away. Notice any scattered thoughts or energy giving way to calm, clear focus.

Bringing your dream to life isn't a process to rush through and get it over with – it's something you want to savor, enjoy, and appreciate every moment of. So take as much time as you need to settle in and really feel present. Allow yourself to feel connected to your immediate environment, to your body, to your soul, and to your dream.

Describe how you're feeling and how this prepares you to bring your dream to life.

Inviting Your Dream

Just as you would invite a much-loved guest into your home, take some time right now to invite your dream into your present experience. You can do this in whatever way feels right to you: Speak welcoming words out loud or say them in your mind. Write an invitation (just as you might send a written invitation for a party or special occasion). Or perhaps you'd like to perform a physical ritual (such as lighting a candle or ringing a bell) to symbolize that you are calling in your dream and devoting this sacred time to nurturing it.

Take as much time as you'd like to welcome your dream into your heart, mind, body, and present experience. Then, write or describe your invitation – and know that your dream is now with you.

Feel Good Now

You can always invite your dream into your life directly (as in the previous prompt). Another way to invite your dream is to simply *feel good* – because your good feelings attract even more positive experiences...such as the fulfillment of your dream!

With this in mind, do something right now that makes you feel good – whether it's connected to your dream or totally unrelated. This can be a physical action (such as writing a gratitude list or doing a silly dance) or something internal (such as recalling a happy memory or imagining a desirable future scene).

Afterwards, describe what you did and how good it made you feel – and know that these good feelings are helping to bring your dream to life!

Permission to Dream

Believe it or not, some people have reservations about dreaming. They might have been taught not to get their hopes up because they'll only be disappointed. Or perhaps they were told that desires are selfish, unspiritual, or simply unrealistic.

Even if you consciously reject such notions, you might still harbor misgivings on some level. But here's where you can emphatically embrace your right to dream and send a clear message that you've got both feet in – by signing the following "permission slip":

I, _____

hereby give myself full permission to dream – joyfully and wholeheartedly!

Signed: _____

Permission to LIVE Your Dream

Even if you've already signed the previous page, giving yourself permission to dream, there's still one more very important piece of permission to grant: the right to not only *have* a dream but to actually *live* it!

These might seem like basically the same thing, but they have a very different energy. (Think of the difference between wanting vs. *having* a lot of money, a loving relationship, optimal wellness, etc.) So, to show that you grant yourself the right to *live* your dream, please sign the following permission slip:

I, _____

hereby give myself full permission to LIVE my dream!

Signed: _____

Defining "Dream"

In the introduction to Part III, we discussed our definition of "dream" (and how we connect dreams with visions and your soul's calling). What matters most here, however, is *your* definition! So, because this entire book (and especially this third part) deals with your dreams, take a moment to answer the question: *What does "dream" mean to you?*

Reframing "Dreams" and "Dreamers"

Just like not everyone gives themselves permission to dream (and to live their dreams), not everyone considers "dreams" and "dreamers" to be positive words. (Think about comments such as, "That's just a dream – it'll never happen," or, "He's a dreamer – he can't function in the real world.")

As favorably as you might define these words, it's still possible to be influenced by others' negative views. So, let's take some time to reframe (or reinforce) these words as the powerful, positive forces that they truly are!

What are some positive words to describe "dreams" and "dreamers" (e.g., visionary, prescience, innovator, imagination, creator)?

Intention

Now that you're in a place (internally and externally) that's conducive to exploring your dream (and you see that dream as wholly positive), take some time to set your intention as you move forward through the remaining portion of this book.

Consider what you'd like to experience during this dream session – including what you'd like to accomplish, what you'd like to allow into your experience, and how you'd like to feel. (For example, you might like to gain clarity about the specifics of your dream, bolster your belief that it will come true, and inspire yourself to take the first steps toward achieving it.)

State your intention out loud and/or write it down. Sit with your intention for a while. Feel its emerging reality – and expect that it (or something even better) will be fulfilled!

Final Preparations

Is there anything else you'd like to do before you embark on the next section of this process? Any hopes, fears, or other thoughts you'd like to express? Any additional rituals or other actions you'd like to perform before moving forward? Take some time to write, do, or express anything that will help you feel fully prepared for the next stage of bringing your dream to life.

Section II:
Reviewing, Revising, and Reinforcing Your Dream

As you began this book, you may have already been clear about your dream, or perhaps this was fairly new territory for you. Now, after having gone through most of this book, you may be feeling absolutely certain about your vision, or perhaps you're still not 100% sure about what your ideal life looks like. Either way is perfectly fine.

Wherever you are right now, this section will help you gain more clarity about your dream. It will give you the opportunity to review and revise your previous ideas and to reinforce the dream that's calling to you right now. And it will help make sure that all of you is aligned and "on board" with your dream – facing in your dream's direction *before* you proceed with your journey!

So, if you're ready to get in touch with your soul's calling and align with your deepest desires, turn the page and dive into your dream!

What is your big-picture calling?

Above any specific goals (e.g., running a marathon or writing a book), what is your overarching desire (e.g., to lovingly uplift and inspire as many people as possible in a joyous way that best utilizes my unique talents and expresses my personal style)?

(Note: You can use this time to reinforce your soul's calling that you came up with in Part I and aligned with in Part II, or revise your calling in any way that most speaks to you right now. Remember, this is a living, breathing process that will continue throughout your entire life!)

How can you express this calling?

There are probably numerous specific ways in which your big-picture calling could manifest. What are some possibilities that might appeal to you?

(For example, if your soul's calling is to share your truth in a way that uplifts and inspires many people, you could express this calling by realizing any number of specific dreams. Perhaps you'd like to do this by writing a bestselling book about your personal philosophy. Or you could become an inspirational public speaker. Or you could express yourself through uplifting music, dance, or art. The possibilities are limitless! Let your imagination soar!)

What specific dream is calling to you now?

Knowing that your big-picture calling will most likely express itself in numerous ways throughout your lifetime, which specific dream (or aspect of your dream) are you feeling most inspired to focus on right now? (Choose from your previous answers, or focus on anything that might be calling to you in this moment.) If this dream came true, what would it look and feel like?

Is this really your dream?

Is this really a *dream* – as opposed to just a moderate, take-it-or-leave-it desire? Does it call to you in the dead of night and follow you throughout your day? Does it really speak to you, light you up, and inspire you to live to your fullest? Do you really, really, REALLY want it?

If so, explain how. If not, how could you revise your dream so that it does ignite your passion for life?

Is this really YOUR dream?

(No, we haven't accidentally repeated a writing prompt – we want to distinguish YOUR dream from someone else's, such as your parents', friends', society's, or anyone who might influence you.)

Consider your dreams – the big calling and the smaller, specific dreams/goals – and ask yourself if they really come from you, your soul, and *your* desires. How much influence have other people had in forming this dream? Are you pursuing this dream to please others (or even a part of yourself that feels that you "should" want this dream), or does it truly come from your own highest/truest self?

Explain how others have influenced you (if at all) in determining this dream and how you might revise your dream (if at all) to make it better reflect YOU.

Sizing Up (or Down) Your Dream

Some dreams are so big that they seem impossible, some are so small that they hardly seem worth it, and others are "just right" (as Goldilocks might say) – big enough to stretch you to live more fully, but not so big that you don't actually expect to realize/live it. (For example, a dream to make $10 today might not inspire you to get out of bed, but wanting to make $10 *billion* today might seem too impossible to even try.)

Is your dream big enough to inspire you but small enough to believe in it? How could you expand your dream to make it more inspiring (but still believable) or scale it back (at least for now) to make it more believable? Or, if it's already in that "just-right" zone, explain how.

Specifying (or Generalizing) Your Dream

Just like you want to find a dream that's neither too big nor too small, you want to find a "sweet spot" between being too specific or too general. If you're too general (e.g., "to make a difference"), the dream might feel vague and uninspiring. If you're too specific (e.g., "to remove lines 74-79 from proposed U.S. Legislation 2016.82C-4"), you might find yourself worrying about nit-picky details, which can deter you from pursuing the dream at all.

With this in mind, how can you make your dream more specific (in order to energize you) or more general (in order to avoid worry)? Or, if your dream is already in that sweet spot on the general/specific spectrum, explain how.

The Story of Your Dream: Seed, Sapling, Tree

Dreams aren't just finished products or ultimate destinations – they're processes, journeys, or stories of growth and evolution. Even the biggest dream starts out as a tiny seed (an idea, a spark, an inspiration), grows into a "sapling" (e.g., a project in the early stages), and eventually matures and blossoms (like a tree that's grown enough to bear fruit).

What's the story of your dream – including its birth, growth, growth, and full fruition? Describe the process its going through, what stage its currently in, what the fully matured dream might look like, and what "fruit" it might yield.

Go to the Feeling Place

Perhaps your fulfilled dream is something that you can experience very soon, or perhaps it will take years to bring about. In either case, there's one part of it that you *can* experience right now: the emotions!

Take some time right now to tap into the emotions that you associate with living your dream (e.g., excitement, enthusiasm, joy, relief, calm). Can you feel right now how you would feel if you were living this scene, this story, this dream life? See if you can go to this feeling place, even just a little bit. Enjoy that feeling, and then see if you can amp it up, even just a bit (e.g., going from *pleased* to *happy*, or from *happy* to *elated*). And then enjoy it some more!

After you've done this, write about your feelings/experiences with this exercise.

Why do you want your dream?
(Part 1: Inspiration)

Most likely, you have many reasons for wanting to live your dream – from external motivations (e.g., to provide a good life for my family) to internal sources of inspiration (e.g., I would feel content, fulfilled, and proud of myself). For now, let's start by looking at your *inspiration* – namely, all the *inner* reasons why you'd like to live your dream. What is your inspiration, and how would you feel if you truly lived your dream?

Why do you want your dream?
(Part 2: "Toward" Motivation)

In addition to your internal reasons (or inspiration) for wanting to live your dream, you probably also have numerous sources of external motivation – including "toward" motivations (things you want) and "away-from" motivations (wanting to avoid undesirable externals). For now, let's look at your "toward" motivation – namely, all the appealing externals that motivate you to live your dream (e.g., to provide for your family). What are some positive external rewards or appealing scenarios that make you want to live your dream?

Why do you want your dream?
(Part 3: "Away-From" Motivation)

While you probably don't want to dwell on these, the desire to avoid negative outcomes (e.g., illness, bankruptcy, or losing a desirable relationship) can provide very powerful "away-from" motivation! What are your "away-from" motivators – namely, all the undesirable externals that you want to avoid by living your dream? After you've identified them, can you rephrase them as positive, "toward" motivators? (For example, if you fear illness, can you motivate yourself to experience optimal health and vitality – either for your own sake or for the sake of the loved ones who'd like to see you healthy?)

Amping Up Your Reasons

Take some time to review your previous three answers – the internal and external reasons why you want to bring your dream to life. How can you intensify these reasons? What would increase your desire for your dream and make you want it even more than you already do? (For example, if you desire optimal health, can you think of all the people who would also benefit from your wellness? How might their lives – and your own – be improved through your well-being?)

Why do you believe that you'll live your dream?

List all the reasons why you think that your dream will come true.

Amping Up Your Belief

Pick one or more of your reasons for believing in your dream (from your previous answer), and amplify it. Write down why these are such convincing reasons, add to them, and do whatever it takes to move from *hoping* or *believing* that your dream will come true to *knowing* it.

Evidence of Dreams Coming True for You

What dreams (big or small) have already come true for you (whether or not they're related to your current dream)?

Exploring the Evidence

Look back at each example from your previous answer and ask: *How'd I do that?*

Was it a systematic process, or did it seem to "just sort of *happen*" through luck or happenstance? What lessons or aspects of these experiences might apply to the process you're going through with bringing your dream to life right now?

Evidence of Other People's Dreams Coming True

When you see dreams coming true for friends, family, colleagues, or even for people you don't know, this helps YOUR dream as well because it provides evidence that *dreams can and DO come true!*

What dreams (big or small, related or unrelated to your dream) have you seen come true in other people's lives? How did they do it? What lessons or aspects of their experiences might apply to you bringing your own dreams to life?

(Note: In addition to convincing yourself that dreams really do come true, one of the best things you can do for your own dreams is to *feel good* when you think about other people's dreams coming true. So, as you answer this question, see if you can celebrate others' successes just as if they were your own.)

Learning from Detours

Just as you can learn from dreams that have come true, you can learn from instances where dreams didn't come true (for you or for others). What lessons can you learn from past "mistakes" (or what once *seemed* like mistakes but may turn out to be valuable teachers)?

To put it another way: how have these detours (intentional or otherwise) helped you to get back on track and moving toward your dreams in the long run? Or, if the detours haven't (yet) helped you get back on track, how might they be able to do so? What inner shifts or external actions would it take for these detours/lessons to help you from this point on?

Aligning with Your Dream

In Part II, you aligned with your soul's calling. Now you're going to see how aligned you are with your *dream* – the specific way in which you'd like to express your soul's calling. (Your alignment may be the same in both cases, or it may be different. For example, you might feel great about a calling to express your truth but feel misgivings about doing so through writing a book.)

When you consider the dream you're currently focusing on, how are the various parts of your internal and external life aligned with it? For example, maybe your thoughts, beliefs, and emotions strongly support your dream, but your environment (work, home life, the company you keep, etc.) presents obstacles.

Rate (from 1-10) how aligned with your dream you are in the major areas of your life (feeling free to elaborate or comment on any of these ratings).

INTERNALS	EXTERNALS
Thoughts:	Physical Health:
Beliefs:	Work:
Emotions:	Relationship(s):
Spirituality:	Home Life:
Other Internal(s)	Other External(s)
_____:	_____:
_____:	_____:
_____:	_____:

Comments:

Amping Up Your Alignment

What changes could you make (internally or externally) to bring your *whole* self into greater alignment with your dream?

(For example, if you have a belief that "nice guys finish last," you could make a list of nice, successful people. Or, if your schedule is overly full, you could choose one or more activities to reduce or eliminate in order to devote more time to pursuing your dream.)

Ready, Willing, and Able?

Are you feeling ready, willing, and able to live your dream – or at least begin the process of leaning into it?

If so, explain why and how. If not, do whatever it takes to clear any doubt, remove any obstacles, and get ready/willing/able – and then explain why/how you are! (And then turn the page and start living your dream!)

Section III:
Living Your Dream

As we said in this book's introduction, "*having* a dream is very different from *living* your dream. It's the difference between longing to visit a dreamy tourist destination and actually going there...or perhaps even *living* there!"

We want you to not only *have* a dream, but to nurture it, to realize it, and to *live* it! We want you to bring your dream to life!

That's what this book's final section is all about: experiencing your dream – now and on an ongoing basis. The writing prompts that follow will invite you to take your dream beyond just a thought or a hope. They will encourage you to turn your dream into reality – to change your thoughts, your words, your actions, your emotions, and your *life* to reflect your greatest aspirations and your highest self.

We hope that these prompts will inspire you to implement positive changes, release negative habits, and keep coming back to your dream...again and again and again!

Already Living the Dream

In what ways are your *already* living your dream (to any extent)?

Already Lived the Dream

In what ways have you lived your current dream (to any extent) in the past? (For example, if your dream is to inspire people by writing a book, maybe you've already written blog posts, magazine articles, or a short ebook.)

Dream Thoughts

What thoughts are most conducive to bringing about – and *living* – your dream? Which ones could you turn into affirmations that you could repeat regularly?

What reminders could you use to help you reinforce these dream-affirming thoughts (e.g., a vision board, post-it notes on your fridge, or emails to yourself)?

Dream Emotions

You can have your dream all "figured out" in your mind, but your heart might not be in it – and living your dream is very difficult if your emotions aren't on board! But if you're feeling good about your life, yourself, your dream, and the direction you're heading in, this process can be an absolute joy!

How do your emotions guide you in living your dream? Have negative emotions steered you away from possible dead ends? Have positive emotions urged you closer to your dream? What guidance are you receiving from your emotions right now regarding your dream?

Inspired Action

What dream-nurturing actions are you feeling *inspired* to take? (In other words, you wouldn't have to force yourself to do them. These are actions that it would almost feel harder *not* to do — almost like stopping a truck that's rolling down a hill — because you're so enthusiastic about them.)

Dream Habits

What habits (thoughts or actions that you think/do on a consistent basis) would help you nurture your dream? How will you implement and habituate them? (For example, you could set an alarm to remind you to write at a certain time each day.)

Triggers

A good way to ingrain a habit is by using a "trigger" – something that you already do that leads into the new habit. (For example, if your dream is to run a marathon, you could go jogging every morning immediately after you brush your teeth – in which case, brushing your teeth would be your trigger.)

What trigger(s) could you use to help you create and reinforce your dream-nourishing habits?

External Support

What externals will you use to support you in bringing your dream to life (e.g., checking in with an accountability partner, joining a support group, or taking a related class)?

Bite-Sized Pieces of the Dream

While your dream may be a smaller version of your big-picture soul's calling, it can still be daunting. So, how do you start living a dream? You can't live it all at once, but you can break it down into small, manageable pieces (e.g., projects, goals, tasks).

How could you divide your dream into "bite-sized" pieces? Which piece would you like to start on first?

Measuring the Dream

A colleague once taught us a valuable lesson: *That which gets measured gets done.*

How will you quantify and measure your progress toward your dream (e.g., pages written, pounds lost, dollars earned, or vacation days taken)?

Daily Check-ins

Ask yourself these two questions each day:

1. *How did I experience my dream today?*

2. *How did I feel?*

Right now, answer these questions for today...and then ask and answer them again tomorrow (and the next day and, ideally, *every* day).

(Our not-very-hidden hope here is that you will generally answer that you did experience your dream and that you felt great while doing it! If you find that this is not generally the case, however, feel free to make whatever shifts help to make positive dream experiences the norm in your daily life!)

Allowing the Dream

We often focus on doing, achieving, and measuring –
all of which can be very helpful. But sometimes what
your dream needs is for you to get out of the way, stop
pushing, and simply allow it to flow to you.

What can you do (or *not* do) to allow your dream to
flow more naturally into your life?

Releasing "Dream Blockers"

Bringing your dream to life is largely a process of addition: adding positive new mental and physical habits into your daily routine. But sometimes it can also be a process of subtracting: minimizing negative thoughts, letting go of toxic relationships, and saying goodbye to anything that blocks you from living your dream.

What "dream blockers" can you subtract from your life? How will you release them?

Recharging Your Dream...and Yourself

What can you do to give yourself a shot of "dream juice" when your spirit (or energy) starts to lag? Do you have a favorite piece of inspiring writing, a vision board, or a supportive friend you can turn to? Do you like to exercise or spend time in nature? Or do you get recharged by simply stepping back, taking some time away from your dream, and then returning refreshed?

In other words, what's your favorite way to recharge? How have you experienced this? When do you next plan on doing this again?

Back on the Dream Wagon

If you find yourself getting off track – moving away from your dream – how can you get "back on the wagon"? (For example, you could rewrite your soul's calling or add to your list of inspiration/motivation for wanting your dream. The only thing we DON'T recommend is getting down on yourself. We all fall down sometimes. The trick is to get back up, keep moving toward your dream, and feel as good as possible while you're doing it!)

Keep Coming Back

Living your dream is not a "one-and-done" deal — you don't figure it out or take a single action and you're set for the rest of your life. It's something that you experience every day. You might drift away or get distracted, but you can always keep coming back to your dream. You might stay focused on your dream, make excellent progress, and live it more and more fully each day — and you still have to (or *get* to) keep coming back to it! You might form new habits or release old ones, change your approach, or even revise your dream itself, but you'll still come back to the essence of it: living life to the fullest and expressing your highest self — your soul's calling.

When and how have you come back to your dream? What can you do to encourage yourself to keep coming back…again and again and again?

Reflecting on Your Journey

How has this journey of bringing your dream to life been for you? Take some time to reflect on (and write about) your experiences while using this book – where you were when you began, where you are now, how it felt for you, what insights you gained, or anything else that came up for you during this process.

Ongoing Check-ins

As we mentioned earlier, living your dream is not a "one-and-done" deal – it's an ongoing process. With this in mind, use this space to check in regularly regarding your dream – your progress, challenges, inspiration, changes, or any other significant experiences.

Conclusion:
The Chain of Dreams

We hope you've enjoyed your journey of discovering your soul's calling, aligning with it, and turning your visions into reality.

Although you've reached the end of this book, you haven't reached the end of your journey. Bringing your dreams to life is a process that you will continue for as long as you live. But this doesn't mean that you won't fulfill your dreams. Quite the contrary! We have every confidence that you will fulfill and live the dream you've been envisioning throughout this book. And when you do fulfill this dream, you will give birth to a new dream (which you will then bring to life and which, in turn will give birth to another dream…and so on and so on and so on) – creating a chain of dreams that will last a lifetime!

At first glance, this situation may seem frustrating. You might think you're setting yourself up for a life of chronic dissatisfaction, like the "hungry ghost" who eats and eats but is never satisfied. But your "chain of dreams" (dreaming and fulfilling dreams and then giving birth to new dreams) can be just the opposite: it can be a life of endless satisfaction, boundless joy, and constant fulfillment.

The key is to appreciate your life and your dreams at every step along the way: to feel enthusiasm ignited by the spark of inspiration when the "seed" of your dream is born and planted within you, to be filled with excitement and pride while watching your "sapling" dream grow and flourish, and to celebrate the full fruition of a dream realized...and then to eagerly anticipate the next dream while continuing to savor the one you're living.

We've been blessed to experience this joyful chain in our own lives. As we discussed in the preface, one of our biggest dreams in recent years was to move to the beach – a dream that we realized just over six months ago. After all that dreaming, planning, and envisioning (and, yes, *waiting*), it sometimes feels a little surreal to actually *be* at the beach – to make the three-minute drive from our house, to put our toes in the sand, to wade in the ocean, to sit and watch the waves rolling in and out, and to exhale and smile...just as we imagined so many times before we arrived!

Yes, it's every bit as glorious as we'd hoped and imagined. But now that we've turned this vision into a reality, does this mean that we've stopped dreaming? Not at all! If anything, it's just the opposite: we now dream more freely than ever! We're also more confident than ever that, as with our beach dreams, our new dreams will also become reality.

Giving birth to these new dreams doesn't mean that we no longer appreciate the beach or the life we've built around it. We savor it every day – for the immediate experience as well as for the wonderful evidence it provides, constantly reminding us of this beautiful truth: *Dreams really do come true!*

We wish the same ongoing joy for you in your own chain of dreams – to cherish the sparks of inspiration, to enjoy the process of bringing your dreams to life, and to savor the fulfilled reality...while feeling eager for the next dream that ignites your heart and soul.

Blessings and gratitude,
Jodi & Dan

About the Authors

Jodi Chapman and Dan Teck are a husband-and-wife team who loves living soulfully and joyfully. Since 2005, they've been living their dream of writing books and creating products that inspire others to connect with their soul and live passionately.

Jodi and Dan are the co-creators of the bestselling *Soulful Journals Series* and the *365 Book Series* as well as *Your Soulful Book*, a heart-centered writing program. Jodi has a B.A. in English and Sociology. She is a certified Law of Attraction Practitioner, an award-winning blogger (www.jodichapman.com), and the author of the books *Soul Bursts* and the upcoming *A Year of Silence*. Dan has an M.F.A. in Creative Writing and a B.A. in Religious Studies. He is also a certified Law of Attraction Practitioner, a certified Life-Optimization Coach, and the author of the book *Rewrite Your Story* and the personal-growth blog *Halfway up the Mountain* (www.halfwayupthemountain.com).

In 2015, they realized their longtime dream of moving to the Oregon coast, where they share their lives with their sweet cats. They feel truly blessed to be able to spend each day doing what they love: hanging out at the beach and working, creating, and playing together.

An Invitation

If one of your dreams is to write a book that inspires others, then we hope you'll sign up for our program! In it, we included everything you'll need to write, finish, and publish your own book!

This program includes monthly live sessions, monthly workbooks, over 30 videos, one-on-one time, a private Facebook community, tons of advice from experts, and so much more! We support you during each step of your outer and inner journey of being a writer, offering concrete writing/marketing tools while guiding you through the emotional highs and lows that you'll experience throughout the process of bringing your soulful book to life.

You've already got the book inside you. Now it's time to get it out of you…and into the world. Your book can change the world, touch hearts, and inspire thousands…but only if you write it! If you're ready to bring your soulful book to life, we would be honored to support you on this life-changing journey! To learn more, visit www.yoursoulfulbook.com.

Made in the USA
Lexington, KY
06 December 2019